Maths
made easy

Key Stage 2
ages 10-11
Workbook 1

Author
John Kennedy

Consultant
Sean McArdle

LONDON • NEW YORK • SYDNEY • MOSCOW • DELHI

Multiplying by 10, 100, and 1000

Write the answers in the boxes.

472 × 10 = 4720   324 × 100 = 32400   57 × 1000 = 57000

Write the answers in the boxes.

426 × 10   =   319 × 10   =   584 × 10   =

740 × 10   =   985 × 10   =   612 × 10   =

102 × 100 =   725 × 100 =   383 × 100 =

909 × 100 =   651 × 100 =   737 × 100 =

4000 × 10 =   5649 × 10 =   8714 × 10 =

6302 × 100 =   9711 × 100 =   4826 × 100 =

Find the number that has been multiplied by 100.

_____ × 100 = 163100   _____ × 100 = 562300

_____ × 100 = 841300   _____ × 100 = 864700

_____ × 100 = 636500   _____ × 100 = 839100

_____ × 100 = 521000   _____ × 100 = 537000

Write the answers in the boxes.

4732 × 1000 =   9105 × 1000 =

6211 × 1000 =   4711 × 1000 =

11264 × 1000 =   84322 × 1000 =

47544 × 1000 =   75543 × 1000 =

59223 × 1000 =   84326 × 1000 =

Find the number that has been multiplied by 1000.

_____ × 1000 = 764000   _____ × 1000 = 9810000

_____ × 1000 = 5372000   _____ × 1000 = 6141000

_____ × 1000 = 4169000   _____ × 1000 = 8399000

The simplest form of fractions

Make these fractions equal by putting a number in the box.

$$\frac{70}{100} = \frac{7}{10} \qquad \frac{4}{12} = \frac{1}{3}$$

Make these fractions equal by putting a number in each box.

$$\frac{30}{100} = \frac{}{10} \qquad \frac{8}{100} = \frac{}{25} \qquad \frac{40}{100} = \frac{}{10} \qquad \frac{15}{100} = \frac{}{20}$$

$$\frac{5}{20} = \frac{}{4} \qquad \frac{25}{100} = \frac{}{4} \qquad \frac{12}{60} = \frac{}{5} \qquad \frac{8}{20} = \frac{}{5}$$

$$\frac{16}{40} = \frac{}{5} \qquad \frac{2}{6} = \frac{}{3} \qquad \frac{10}{60} = \frac{}{6} \qquad \frac{2}{12} = \frac{}{6}$$

$$\frac{9}{18} = \frac{}{2} \qquad \frac{12}{18} = \frac{}{3} \qquad \frac{4}{24} = \frac{}{6} \qquad \frac{7}{28} = \frac{}{4}$$

$$\frac{4}{6} = \frac{2}{} \qquad \frac{6}{10} = \frac{3}{} \qquad \frac{9}{15} = \frac{3}{} \qquad \frac{8}{12} = \frac{2}{}$$

$$\frac{18}{20} = \frac{9}{} \qquad \frac{21}{28} = \frac{3}{} \qquad \frac{6}{8} = \frac{3}{} \qquad \frac{5}{50} = \frac{1}{}$$

$$\frac{15}{25} = \frac{3}{} \qquad \frac{4}{16} = \frac{1}{} \qquad \frac{12}{20} = \frac{3}{} \qquad \frac{12}{18} = \frac{2}{}$$

$$\frac{3}{15} = \frac{1}{} \qquad \frac{9}{36} = \frac{1}{} \qquad \frac{9}{27} = \frac{1}{} \qquad \frac{30}{50} = \frac{3}{}$$

Make these rows of fractions equal by putting a number in each box.

$$\frac{1}{9} = \frac{}{18} = \frac{3}{} = \frac{}{36} = \frac{}{45} = \frac{6}{}$$

$$\frac{1}{10} = \frac{}{20} = \frac{3}{} = \frac{4}{} = \frac{}{50} = \frac{}{60}$$

$$\frac{3}{5} = \frac{12}{} = \frac{}{25} = \frac{18}{} = \frac{}{35} = \frac{24}{}$$

$$\frac{5}{6} = \frac{}{12} = \frac{15}{} = \frac{20}{} = \frac{25}{} = \frac{30}{}$$

$$\frac{1}{7} = \frac{}{14} = \frac{}{21} = \frac{}{28} = \frac{5}{} = \frac{}{42}$$

$$\frac{3}{11} = \frac{}{44} = \frac{}{77} = \frac{27}{} = \frac{}{110} = \frac{33}{}$$

Changing improper fractions to mixed numbers

Change this top-heavy fraction to a mixed number.
(Remember you may need to cancel.)

$$\frac{27}{12} = 2\frac{\cancel{3}^{1}}{\cancel{12}_{4}} = 2\frac{1}{4}$$

Change these mixed numbers to top-heavy fractions.

$$2\frac{3}{4} = \frac{11}{4} \qquad\qquad 4\frac{1}{2} = \frac{9}{2}$$

Change these top-heavy fractions to mixed numbers.

$$\frac{25}{3} = \qquad\qquad \frac{15}{12} = \qquad\qquad \frac{40}{7} =$$

$$\frac{17}{6} = \qquad\qquad \frac{11}{9} = \qquad\qquad \frac{12}{5} =$$

$$\frac{27}{5} = \qquad\qquad \frac{26}{3} = \qquad\qquad \frac{32}{5} =$$

$$\frac{9}{2} = \qquad\qquad \frac{19}{2} = \qquad\qquad \frac{15}{4} =$$

$$\frac{30}{4} = \qquad\qquad \frac{26}{8} = \qquad\qquad \frac{42}{9} =$$

Change these mixed numbers to top-heavy fractions.

$$4\frac{3}{4} = \qquad\qquad 9\frac{1}{2} = \qquad\qquad 12\frac{1}{4} =$$

$$3\frac{2}{3} = \qquad\qquad 6\frac{3}{4} = \qquad\qquad 3\frac{9}{10} =$$

$$5\frac{1}{8} = \qquad\qquad 3\frac{2}{5} = \qquad\qquad 2\frac{5}{6} =$$

$$5\frac{1}{4} = \qquad\qquad 3\frac{3}{8} = \qquad\qquad 2\frac{11}{12} =$$

$$2\frac{7}{10} = \qquad\qquad 4\frac{3}{10} = \qquad\qquad 4\frac{1}{8} =$$

$$7\frac{3}{4} = \qquad\qquad 8\frac{1}{2} = \qquad\qquad 1\frac{5}{12} =$$

Rounding decimals

Write these decimals to the nearest tenth.

9.21 is   4.38 is   2.47 is

3.48 is   8.17 is   6.28 is

7.14 is   3.91 is   2.56 is

8.41 is   2.36 is   1.53 is

Write these decimals to the nearest tenth.

9.35 is   8.71 is   6.05 is

1.19 is   3.65 is   4.21 is

8.55 is   7.35 is   9.14 is

6.83 is   2.15 is   6.34 is

Write these decimals to the nearest tenth.

25.61 is   14.35 is   11.24 is

16.85 is   24.34 is   71.36 is

26.85 is   11.54 is   37.25 is

92.42 is   95.65 is   27.36 is

45.17 is   36.75 is   22.05 is

Adding with different numbers of digits

Work out the answer to each sum.

```
  432          176
+  43        +  97
-----        -----
  475          273
              1 1
```

Remember to carry if you need to.

Work out the answer to each sum.

```
  148        271        371        938
+  31      +  17      +  24      +  31
-----      -----      -----      -----


  942        747        633        101
+  26      +  34      +  43      +  75
-----      -----      -----      -----
```

Write the answer in the box.

$$47 + 320 =$$

$$273 + 97 =$$

$$26 + 251 =$$

$$849 + 38 =$$

Write in the missing numbers in these sums.

```
  2 4 2          9 3          8   5          6   4
+   2 7        + 3 8        +   1 2        +   6 3
-------        -----        -------        -------
  2   9          9 7 7        8 3 7          6 8 7
```

Work out the answer to each sum. Use the space for working out.

Tommy has saved £238. For his birthday he is given another £52. How much does he have altogether?

A circus sells 208 adult tickets and 86 children's tickets. How many tickets are sold altogether?

6

Adding with different numbers of digits

Work out the answer to each sum.

```
  652          77
+  73        + 845
 ─────       ─────
  725         922
    1          1 1
```

Remember to carry if you need to.

Work out the answer to each sum.

```
   98         548          75          921
+ 645       +  72       + 426        +  47
─────       ─────       ─────        ─────
```

```
  842          71          64           87
+  74       + 326       + 819        + 520
─────       ─────       ─────        ─────
```

Write the answer in the box.

594 + 72 =   65 + 948 =

63 + 341 =   87 + 485 =

Write in the missing numbers in these sums.

```
     7          46            9          376
  3 2 8      +   4 2       + 7 3       +     9
  ─────      ───────       ─────       ───────
  3 6 5        6 8          9 6 5         4 5
```

Work out the answer to each sum. Use the space for working out.

Jennifer has 936 stamps in her collection. Dennis has 98. How many do they have altogether?

There are 576 cans of soup on a supermarket shelf. A shop worker puts out another 87. How many cans are now on the shelf?

Subtracting one number from another

Work out the answer to each sum.

$$\begin{array}{r} {}^{7}\!\!\!\!{}^{1}8\!\!\!\!34 \\ -\ \ 44 \\ \hline 790 \end{array} \qquad \begin{array}{r} {}^{3}\!\!\!\!{}^{1}4\!\!\!\!{}^{2}\!\!\!\!{}^{1}31 \\ -\ \ 84 \\ \hline 347 \end{array}$$

Work out the answer to each sum.

$$\begin{array}{r} 835 \\ -\ 23 \\ \hline \end{array} \qquad \begin{array}{r} 490 \\ -\ 70 \\ \hline \end{array} \qquad \begin{array}{r} 175 \\ -\ 54 \\ \hline \end{array} \qquad \begin{array}{r} 428 \\ -\ 67 \\ \hline \end{array}$$

$$\begin{array}{r} 587 \\ -\ 43 \\ \hline \end{array} \qquad \begin{array}{r} 674 \\ -\ 62 \\ \hline \end{array} \qquad \begin{array}{r} 389 \\ -\ 58 \\ \hline \end{array} \qquad \begin{array}{r} 270 \\ -\ 30 \\ \hline \end{array}$$

$$\begin{array}{r} 483 \\ -\ 35 \\ \hline \end{array} \qquad \begin{array}{r} 951 \\ -\ 28 \\ \hline \end{array} \qquad \begin{array}{r} 746 \\ -\ 17 \\ \hline \end{array} \qquad \begin{array}{r} 234 \\ -\ 16 \\ \hline \end{array}$$

Write the answer in the box.

$491 - 31 =$ 　　　　　　　$654 - 22 =$

$874 - 63 =$ 　　　　　　　$577 - 26 =$

Work out the answer to each sum.

There are 565 children in a school.
If 36 children are on a residential trip,
how many children are still at school?

A DIY store has 247 tins of paint.
If they sell 29 tins, how many will
they have left?

Subtracting one number from another

Work out the answer to each sum.

$$\begin{array}{r} {}^{3}{\!/}^{1} \\ 5\cancel{4}31 \\ -\ 250 \\ \hline 5181 \end{array} \qquad \begin{array}{r} {}^{5}{\!/}^{2}{}^{1} \\ 9\cancel{6}\cancel{3}5 \\ -\ 78 \\ \hline 9557 \end{array}$$

Work out the answer to each sum.

$$\begin{array}{r} 5\,415 \\ -\ 222 \\ \hline \end{array} \qquad \begin{array}{r} 3\,629 \\ -\ 147 \\ \hline \end{array} \qquad \begin{array}{r} 2\,437 \\ -\ 282 \\ \hline \end{array} \qquad \begin{array}{r} 6\,451 \\ -\ 260 \\ \hline \end{array}$$

$$\begin{array}{r} 9\,523 \\ -\ 347 \\ \hline \end{array} \qquad \begin{array}{r} 7\,846 \\ -\ 557 \\ \hline \end{array} \qquad \begin{array}{r} 2\,914 \\ -\ 526 \\ \hline \end{array} \qquad \begin{array}{r} 8\,854 \\ -\ 298 \\ \hline \end{array}$$

$$\begin{array}{r} 5\,371 \\ -\ 617 \\ \hline \end{array} \qquad \begin{array}{r} 9\,294 \\ -\ 435 \\ \hline \end{array} \qquad \begin{array}{r} 8\,685 \\ -\ 737 \\ \hline \end{array} \qquad \begin{array}{r} 5\,491 \\ -\ 639 \\ \hline \end{array}$$

Write the answer in the box.

$5\,643 - 26 =$ ____ $8\,437 - 18 =$ ____ $7\,781 - 92 =$ ____

$9\,782 - 44 =$ ____ $1\,941 - 22 =$ ____ $6\,954 - 75 =$ ____

Work out the answer to each sum.

2826 people went to see a pop concert. 135 had to leave early to catch their train. How many were left at the end?

Mr Brown wins £9546 in a lottery. If he spends £627 on a holiday, how much will he have left?

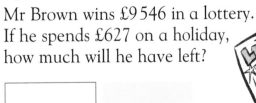

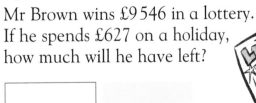

Real life problems

Toby has £525.95 in the bank and he spends £146.37 on a holiday. How much does he have left?

Toby has £379.58 left.

$$\begin{array}{r} {}^{4}\cancel{5}{}^{11}\cancel{2}{}^{1}5.{}^{8}\cancel{9}{}^{1}5 \\ -\ £146.37 \\ \hline £379.58 \end{array}$$

A rally driver drives 294 km on the first day of a race and 236 km on the second day. How many kilometres does he travel in the two days?

He drives 530 km.

$$\begin{array}{r} 294km \\ +\ 236km \\ \hline 530km \\ {}_{1\ \ 1} \end{array}$$

Mia spends £1 525 on a new computer and £146 on a printer. How much does she spend altogether?

Derek has a piece of wood which is 3.46 m long to make a shelf to fit an alcove 2.63 m long. How much must he cut off his piece of wood in order for it to fit?

A family is on a touring holiday. If they travel 576 km in the first week and 625 km in the second week, how many kilometres have they travelled altogether?

If their car had already done 27 421 km before the holiday, how many kilometres will it have done by the end?

Two boxers are weighed before a boxing match. If the first weighs 86.43 kg and the second weighs 84.35 kg, what is the difference between their weights?

Real life problems

An electrician buys 415 m of cable. If he uses
234 m, how much does he have left?

$$\begin{array}{r} \overset{3\ 1}{\cancel{4}}15 \text{ m} \\ -\ 234 \text{ m} \\ \hline 181 \text{ m} \end{array}$$

He has 181 m of cable left.

Simon travels by train for 110 km, by bus
for 56 km and then walks the final 5 km.
How far does he travel?

$$\begin{array}{r} 110 \text{ km} \\ 56 \text{ km} \\ +\ \ \ 5 \text{ km} \\ \hline 171 \text{ km} \\ {\scriptstyle 1} \end{array}$$

Simon travels 171 km.

Mr Hindley works 185 hours a month.
His wife works 73 hours a month. How many
hours do they work altogether in a month?

A school collects money for the local hospice. If the pupils
collect £275 in the first month, £210 in the second month, and
£136 in the third month, how much do they collect altogether?

Danny and Ruth both have electric car
racing sets. If Danny has 12.75 m of
track and Ruth has 14.83 m of track,
how much more track does Ruth
have than Danny?

How much track will they have if they put both sets together?

A builder buys 8 755 kg of sand, but only
uses 6 916 kg. How much does he have left?

11

Real life problems

David, Andrew, and Hilary want to put their money together to buy a present for their brother. If David gives £12.50, Andrew gives £14.75, and Hilary gives £15.25, how much will they have to spend?

```
   £12.50
   £14.75
+  £15.25
   £42.50
   1 1 1
```

They will have £42.50 to spend.

A shop has 6.75 kg of curry powder and sells 2.50 kg. How much does it have left?

```
   6.75 kg
 - 2.50 kg
   4.25 kg
```

The shop has 4.25 kg left.

A shop orders 145 kg of sugar, 565 kg of salt, and 926 kg of butter. What is the total weight of the order?

Mr Cohen's garage is 3.76 m long and his car is 4.79 m long. By how much is his car too long for his garage?

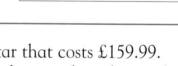

A holiday in Florida costs £876. A holiday in Majorca costs £394. How much more expensive is the Florida holiday?

Bethany is saving up to buy a guitar that costs £159.99. If she already has £65.37, how much more does she need?

Mr Robinson's garden is 9.52 m wide. His neighbour's garden is 8.47 m wide. If they take down the fence and share their gardens, how wide will the new garden be?

Decimal addition

Write in the answers to these sums.

```
  47.15          43.99
+ 19.36        + 12.76
-------        -------
  66.51          56.75
  1   1          1  1
```

Write the answer to each sum.

53.72	84.17	29.36	23.56	62.49
+77.92	+68.21	+66.84	+79.14	+18.75

35.67	29.88	67.39	49.32	27.22
+ 12.99	+43.02	+81.70	+14.95	+38.84

Write the answer to each sum.

76.30	44.29	81.97	29.86	68.25
+22.97	+11.04	+69.14	+76.33	+84.36

83.90	45.83	52.17	84.93	72.83
+30.24	+45.71	+90.21	+29.37	+41.16

Write the answer to each sum.

37.89 + 82.15 =   32.44 + 21.88 =   37.19 + 28.24 =

68.67 + 29.82 =   21.99 + 79.32 =   52.45 + 34.58 =

84.77 + 39.12 =   63.84 + 29.81 =   34.43 + 25.64 =

33.97 + 24.62 =   76.39 + 43.78 =   52.38 + 38.43 =

Decimal addition

Write the answer to each sum.

```
  296.48          173.05
+ 131.74        + 269.23
  428.22          442.28
  1 1 1            1 1
```

Write the answer to each sum.

```
  491.83          964.71          302.04          306.25
+ 137.84        + 321.26        + 204.99        + 844.24
```

```
  471.93          842.01          675.82          137.82
+ 755.26        + 711.84        + 105.23        + 399.71
```

```
  465.24          178.93          184.74          443.27
+ 605.27        + 599.41        + 372.81        + 705.99
```

```
  563.23          703.95          825.36          529.33
+ 413.98        + 685.11        + 249.85        + 482.56
```

Write the answer to each sum.

$421.79 + 136.25 =$ $192.31 + 241.73 =$

$558.32 + 137.94 =$ $501.84 + 361.93 =$

$227.66 + 142.07 =$ $275.31 + 239.33 =$

$153.31 + 189.02 =$ $491.44 + 105.37 =$

$253.71 + 562.41 =$ $829.25 + 163.74 =$

Decimal subtraction

Write the answer to each sum.

64.92	64.21	73.71	92.63
− 26.35	− 16.02	− 19.24	− 67.14
45.76	73.52	98.98	53.58
− 16.18	− 39.27	− 39.19	− 14.39
94.87	21.74	62.35	81.94
− 65.28	− 12.15	− 13.16	− 28.15
62.95	81.42	48.52	61.55
− 33.37	− 25.04	− 14.49	− 13.26

Write the answer to each sum.

51.52 − 12.13 =   72.41 − 23.18 =

91.91 − 22.22 =   53.84 − 19.65 =

41.82 − 18.13 =   51.61 − 23.14 =

83.91 − 14.73 =   64.65 − 37.26 =

53.21 − 35.12 =   77.31 − 28.15 =

Decimal subtraction

Write the answer to each sum.

$$\begin{array}{r} \overset{7}{6}\overset{1}{8}.17 \\ - 11.43 \\ \hline 56.74 \end{array} \qquad \begin{array}{r} \overset{8}{3}\overset{1}{9}.24 \\ - 13.51 \\ \hline 25.73 \end{array}$$

Write the answer to each sum.

$$\begin{array}{r} 87.23 \\ - 24.41 \\ \hline \end{array} \qquad \begin{array}{r} 95.15 \\ - 31.35 \\ \hline \end{array} \qquad \begin{array}{r} 66.37 \\ - 21.93 \\ \hline \end{array} \qquad \begin{array}{r} 85.15 \\ - 26.32 \\ \hline \end{array}$$

$$\begin{array}{r} 72.28 \\ - 21.36 \\ \hline \end{array} \qquad \begin{array}{r} 63.14 \\ - 32.41 \\ \hline \end{array} \qquad \begin{array}{r} 99.22 \\ - 33.70 \\ \hline \end{array} \qquad \begin{array}{r} 62.19 \\ - 29.34 \\ \hline \end{array}$$

$$\begin{array}{r} 77.36 \\ - 24.42 \\ \hline \end{array} \qquad \begin{array}{r} 55.49 \\ - 27.66 \\ \hline \end{array} \qquad \begin{array}{r} 68.25 \\ - 31.51 \\ \hline \end{array} \qquad \begin{array}{r} 41.14 \\ - 13.20 \\ \hline \end{array}$$

$$\begin{array}{r} 82.35 \\ - 23.41 \\ \hline \end{array} \qquad \begin{array}{r} 63.29 \\ - 15.36 \\ \hline \end{array} \qquad \begin{array}{r} 53.64 \\ - 23.72 \\ \hline \end{array} \qquad \begin{array}{r} 35.61 \\ - 26.19 \\ \hline \end{array}$$

Write the answer to each sum.

$63.46 - 24.51 =$ $92.19 - 63.28 =$

$91.35 - 33.42 =$ $41.24 - 14.30 =$

$52.25 - 23.42 =$ $72.63 - 53.71 =$

$92.84 - 23.93 =$ $61.16 - 24.42 =$

$81.81 - 55.90 =$ $94.31 - 27.40 =$

Answer Section with Parents' Notes
Key Stage 2
Ages 10–11
Book 1

This 8-page section provides answers to all the activities in this book. This will enable you to mark your children's work or can be used by them if they prefer to do their own marking.

The notes for each page help explain the common pitfalls and problems and, where appropriate, give indications as to what practice is needed to ensure your children understand where they have gone wrong.

---

2 ☆ Multiplying by 10, 100, and 1000

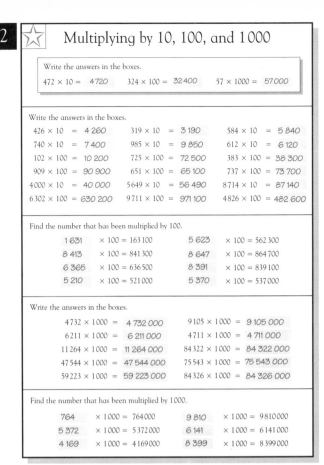

Write the answers in the boxes.

$472 \times 10 = 4720$ $324 \times 100 = 32400$ $57 \times 1000 = 57000$

Write the answers in the boxes.

$426 \times 10 = 4260$	$319 \times 10 = 3190$	$584 \times 10 = 5840$
$740 \times 10 = 7400$	$985 \times 10 = 9850$	$612 \times 10 = 6120$
$102 \times 100 = 10200$	$725 \times 100 = 72500$	$383 \times 100 = 38300$
$909 \times 100 = 90900$	$651 \times 100 = 65100$	$737 \times 100 = 73700$
$4000 \times 10 = 40000$	$5649 \times 10 = 56490$	$8714 \times 10 = 87140$
$6302 \times 100 = 630200$	$9711 \times 100 = 971100$	$4826 \times 100 = 482600$

Find the number that has been multiplied by 100.

$1631 \times 100 = 163100$	$5623 \times 100 = 562300$
$8413 \times 100 = 841300$	$8647 \times 100 = 864700$
$6365 \times 100 = 636500$	$8391 \times 100 = 839100$
$5210 \times 100 = 521000$	$5370 \times 100 = 537000$

Write the answers in the boxes.

$4732 \times 1000 = 4732000$	$9105 \times 1000 = 9105000$
$6211 \times 1000 = 6211000$	$4711 \times 1000 = 4711000$
$11264 \times 1000 = 11264000$	$84322 \times 1000 = 84322000$
$47544 \times 1000 = 47544000$	$75543 \times 1000 = 75543000$
$59223 \times 1000 = 59223000$	$84326 \times 1000 = 84326000$

Find the number that has been multiplied by 1000.

$764 \times 1000 = 764000$	$9810 \times 1000 = 9810000$
$5372 \times 1000 = 5372000$	$6141 \times 1000 = 6141000$
$4169 \times 1000 = 4169000$	$8399 \times 1000 = 8399000$

The child should realise that multiplying by 10, 100, or 1000 is the same as adding one, two, or three noughts. In order to do the second and last sections, the child will need to divide the answers to find the number that has been multiplied.

---

3 The simplest form of fractions ☆

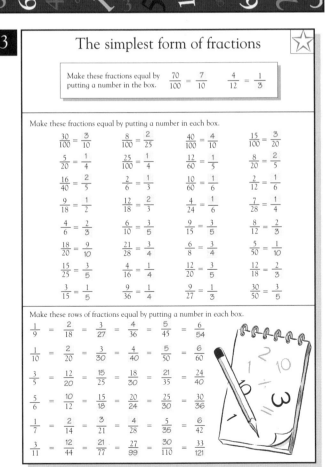

Make these fractions equal by putting a number in the box.

$\frac{70}{100} = \frac{7}{10}$ $\frac{4}{12} = \frac{1}{3}$

Make these fractions equal by putting a number in each box.

$\frac{30}{100} = \frac{3}{10}$	$\frac{8}{100} = \frac{2}{25}$	$\frac{40}{100} = \frac{4}{10}$	$\frac{15}{100} = \frac{3}{20}$
$\frac{5}{20} = \frac{1}{4}$	$\frac{25}{100} = \frac{1}{4}$	$\frac{12}{60} = \frac{1}{5}$	$\frac{8}{20} = \frac{2}{5}$
$\frac{16}{40} = \frac{2}{5}$	$\frac{2}{6} = \frac{1}{3}$	$\frac{10}{60} = \frac{1}{6}$	$\frac{2}{12} = \frac{1}{6}$
$\frac{9}{18} = \frac{1}{2}$	$\frac{12}{18} = \frac{2}{3}$	$\frac{4}{24} = \frac{1}{6}$	$\frac{7}{28} = \frac{1}{4}$
$\frac{4}{6} = \frac{2}{3}$	$\frac{6}{10} = \frac{3}{5}$	$\frac{9}{15} = \frac{3}{5}$	$\frac{8}{12} = \frac{2}{3}$
$\frac{18}{20} = \frac{9}{10}$	$\frac{21}{28} = \frac{3}{4}$	$\frac{6}{8} = \frac{3}{4}$	$\frac{5}{50} = \frac{1}{10}$
$\frac{15}{25} = \frac{3}{5}$	$\frac{4}{16} = \frac{1}{4}$	$\frac{12}{20} = \frac{3}{5}$	$\frac{12}{18} = \frac{2}{3}$
$\frac{3}{15} = \frac{1}{5}$	$\frac{9}{36} = \frac{1}{4}$	$\frac{9}{27} = \frac{1}{3}$	$\frac{30}{50} = \frac{3}{5}$

Make these rows of fractions equal by putting a number in each box.

$\frac{1}{9} = \frac{2}{18} = \frac{3}{27} = \frac{4}{36} = \frac{5}{45} = \frac{6}{54}$

$\frac{1}{10} = \frac{2}{20} = \frac{3}{30} = \frac{4}{40} = \frac{5}{50} = \frac{6}{60}$

$\frac{3}{5} = \frac{12}{20} = \frac{15}{25} = \frac{18}{30} = \frac{21}{35} = \frac{24}{40}$

$\frac{5}{6} = \frac{10}{12} = \frac{15}{18} = \frac{20}{24} = \frac{25}{30} = \frac{30}{36}$

$\frac{1}{7} = \frac{2}{14} = \frac{3}{21} = \frac{4}{28} = \frac{5}{35} = \frac{6}{42}$

$\frac{3}{11} = \frac{12}{44} = \frac{21}{77} = \frac{27}{99} = \frac{30}{110} = \frac{33}{121}$

If the child has problems with this page, explain to them that fractions remain the same as long as you multiply or divide the numerator and denominator by the same number.

---

4 ☆ Changing improper fractions to mixed numbers

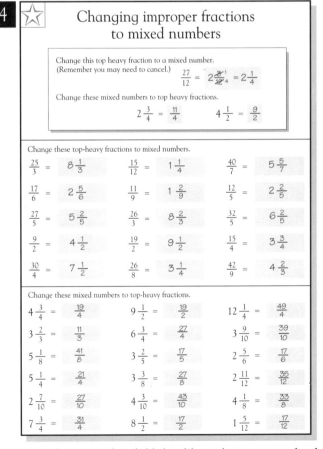

Change this top heavy fraction to a mixed number. (Remember you may need to cancel.) $\frac{27}{12} = 2\frac{3}{12} = 2\frac{1}{4}$

Change these mixed numbers to top heavy fractions.

$2\frac{3}{4} = \frac{11}{4}$ $4\frac{1}{2} = \frac{9}{2}$

Change these top-heavy fractions to mixed numbers.

$\frac{25}{3} = 8\frac{1}{3}$	$\frac{15}{12} = 1\frac{1}{4}$	$\frac{40}{7} = 5\frac{5}{7}$
$\frac{17}{6} = 2\frac{5}{6}$	$\frac{11}{9} = 1\frac{2}{9}$	$\frac{12}{5} = 2\frac{2}{5}$
$\frac{27}{5} = 5\frac{2}{5}$	$\frac{26}{3} = 8\frac{2}{3}$	$\frac{32}{5} = 6\frac{2}{5}$
$\frac{9}{2} = 4\frac{1}{2}$	$\frac{19}{2} = 9\frac{1}{2}$	$\frac{15}{4} = 3\frac{3}{4}$
$\frac{30}{4} = 7\frac{1}{2}$	$\frac{26}{8} = 3\frac{1}{4}$	$\frac{42}{9} = 4\frac{2}{3}$

Change these mixed numbers to top-heavy fractions.

$4\frac{3}{4} = \frac{19}{4}$	$9\frac{1}{2} = \frac{19}{2}$	$12\frac{1}{4} = \frac{49}{4}$
$3\frac{2}{3} = \frac{11}{3}$	$6\frac{3}{4} = \frac{27}{4}$	$3\frac{9}{10} = \frac{39}{10}$
$5\frac{1}{8} = \frac{41}{8}$	$3\frac{2}{5} = \frac{17}{5}$	$2\frac{5}{6} = \frac{17}{6}$
$5\frac{1}{4} = \frac{21}{4}$	$3\frac{3}{8} = \frac{27}{8}$	$2\frac{11}{12} = \frac{35}{12}$
$2\frac{7}{10} = \frac{27}{10}$	$4\frac{3}{10} = \frac{43}{10}$	$4\frac{1}{8} = \frac{33}{8}$
$7\frac{3}{4} = \frac{31}{4}$	$8\frac{1}{2} = \frac{17}{2}$	$1\frac{5}{12} = \frac{17}{12}$

In the first part, the child should see that you can divide the denominator into the numerator and place the remainder over the denominator. Use card circles cut into equal parts to reinforce the idea, e.g. how many whole circles can you make from 17 quarter circles?

Rounding decimals

Write these decimals to the nearest tenth.

6.23 is 6.2   6.27 is 6.3

If the second decimal place is a 5, we round up the first decimal place to the number above.

6.25 is 6.3

Write these decimals to the nearest tenth.

9.21 is	9.2	4.38 is	4.4	2.47 is	2.5
3.48 is	3.5	8.17 is	8.2	6.28 is	6.3
7.14 is	7.1	3.91 is	3.9	2.56 is	2.6
8.41 is	8.4	2.36 is	2.4	1.53 is	1.5

Write these decimals to the nearest tenth.

9.35 is	9.4	8.71 is	8.7	6.05 is	6.1
1.19 is	1.2	3.65 is	3.7	4.21 is	4.2
8.55 is	8.6	7.35 is	7.4	9.14 is	9.1
6.83 is	6.8	2.15 is	2.2	6.34 is	6.3

Write these decimals to the nearest tenth.

25.61 is	25.6	14.35 is	14.4	11.24 is	11.2
16.85 is	16.9	24.34 is	24.3	71.36 is	71.4
26.85 is	26.9	11.54 is	11.5	37.25 is	37.3
92.42 is	92.4	95.65 is	95.7	27.36 is	27.4
45.17 is	45.2	36.75 is	36.8	22.05 is	22.1

If the child experiences difficulty, point out that the significant digit to look at is in the second decimal place. The use of a number line may be helpful where the child is still unsure. In the second section, the concept of .05 is introduced. This must be rounded up.

Adding with different numbers of digits

Work out the answer to each sum.

```
  432          176
+  43        +  97
  475          273
               1 1
```

Remember to carry if you need to.

Work out the answer to each sum.

```
  148       271       371       938
+  31     +  17     +  24     +  31
  179       288       395       969
```

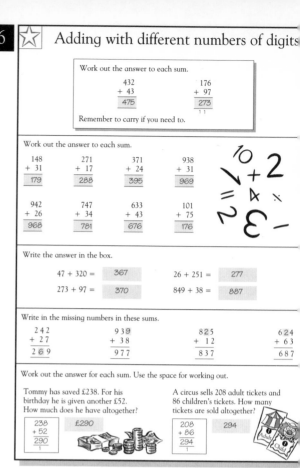

```
  942       747       633       101
+  26     +  34     +  43     +  75
  968       781       676       176
```

Write the answer in the box.

47 + 320 = 367   26 + 251 = 277

273 + 97 = 370   849 + 38 = 887

Write in the missing numbers in these sums.

```
  242        939        825        624
+  27      +  38      +  12      +  63
  269        977        837        687
```

Work out the answer for each sum. Use the space for working out.

Tommy has saved £238. For his birthday he is given another £52. How much does he have altogether?

```
  238
+  52
  290
   1
```
£290

A circus sells 208 adult tickets and 86 children's tickets. How many tickets are sold altogether?

```
  208
+  86
  294
   1
```
294

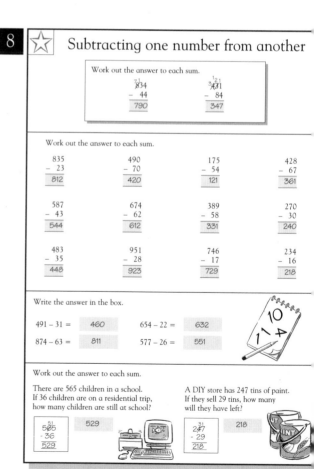

This page and the next should be straightforward. Any errors will probably be due to a failure to carry or, particularly in the second section, may occur wh the child has added digits with different place valu

Adding with different numbers of digits

Work out the answer to each sum.

```
  652          77
+  73       + 845
  725         922
   1          1 1
```

Remember to carry if you need to.

Work out the answer to each sum.

```
   98       548        75       921
+ 645     +  72     + 426     +  47
  743       620       501       968
```

```
  842        71        64        87
+  74     + 326     + 819     + 520
  916       397       883       607
```

Write the answer in the box.

594 + 72 = 666   65 + 948 = 1 013

63 + 341 = 404   87 + 485 = 572

Write in the missing numbers in these sums.

```
   37        646        892        376
+ 328      +  42      +  73      +  69
  365        688        965        445
```

Work out the answer for each sum. Use the space for working out.

Jennifer has 936 stamps in her collection. Dennis has 98. How many do they have altogether?

```
  936
+  98
 1034
  1 1
```
1 034

There are 576 cans of soup on a supermarket shelf. A shop worker puts out another 87. How many cans are now on the shelf?

```
  576
+  87
  663
  1 1
```
663

As with the previous page, any errors here will probably be due to a failure to carry numbers over. Other errors may be due to the child adding digits with different place values.

Subtracting one number from another

Work out the answer to each sum.

```
  7 1
  8̸34          4̸3̸1
-  44         -  84
  790           347
```

Work out the answer to each sum.

```
  835       490       175       428
-  23     -  70     -  54     -  67
  812       420       121       361
```

```
  587       674       389       270
-  43     -  62     -  58     -  30
  544       612       331       240
```

```
  483       951       746       234
-  35     -  28     -  17     -  16
  448       923       729       218
```

Write the answer in the box.

491 – 31 = 460   654 – 22 = 632

874 – 63 = 811   577 – 26 = 551

Work out the answer to each sum.

There are 565 children in a school. If 36 children are on a residential trip, how many children are still at school?

```
  5̸6̸5
-  36
  529
```
529

A DIY store has 247 tins of paint. If they sell 29 tins, how many will they have left?

```
  2̸4̸7
-  29
  218
```
218

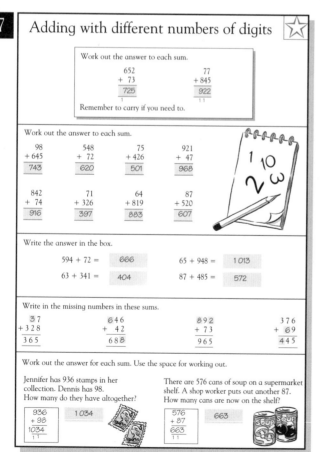

The most likely errors to occur in the first section will involve subtractions where a larger digit has t be taken away from a smaller digit. Children ofter take the smaller digit which is on the top away from the larger digit on the bottom.

Subtracting one number from another ☆

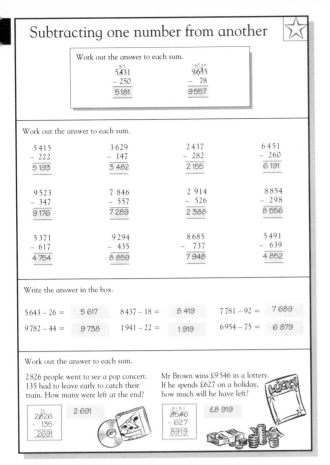

Work out the answer to each sum.

$$\begin{array}{r} {}^{3\,1}5\,431 \\ -\ \ 250 \\ \hline 5\,181 \end{array} \qquad \begin{array}{r} {}^{5\,1\,2\,1}9\,635 \\ -\ \ \ \ 78 \\ \hline 9\,557 \end{array}$$

Work out the answer to each sum.

$$\begin{array}{r} 5\,415 \\ -\ 222 \\ \hline 5\,193 \end{array} \qquad \begin{array}{r} 3\,629 \\ -\ 147 \\ \hline 3\,482 \end{array} \qquad \begin{array}{r} 2\,437 \\ -\ 282 \\ \hline 2\,155 \end{array} \qquad \begin{array}{r} 6\,451 \\ -\ 260 \\ \hline 6\,191 \end{array}$$

$$\begin{array}{r} 9\,523 \\ -\ 347 \\ \hline 9\,176 \end{array} \qquad \begin{array}{r} 7\,846 \\ -\ 557 \\ \hline 7\,289 \end{array} \qquad \begin{array}{r} 2\,914 \\ -\ 526 \\ \hline 2\,388 \end{array} \qquad \begin{array}{r} 8\,854 \\ -\ 298 \\ \hline 8\,556 \end{array}$$

$$\begin{array}{r} 5\,371 \\ -\ 617 \\ \hline 4\,754 \end{array} \qquad \begin{array}{r} 9\,294 \\ -\ 435 \\ \hline 8\,859 \end{array} \qquad \begin{array}{r} 8\,685 \\ -\ 737 \\ \hline 7\,948 \end{array} \qquad \begin{array}{r} 5\,491 \\ -\ 639 \\ \hline 4\,852 \end{array}$$

Write the answer in the box.

5 643 − 26 = 5 617   8 437 − 18 = 8 419   7 781 − 92 = 7 689

9 782 − 44 = 9 738   1 941 − 22 = 1 919   6 954 − 75 = 6 879

Work out the answer to each sum.

2826 people went to see a pop concert. 135 had to leave early to catch their train. How many were left at the end?

$$\begin{array}{r} {}^{7\,1}2\,826 \\ -\ \ 135 \\ \hline 2\,691 \end{array}$$ 2 691

Mr Brown wins £9 546 in a lottery. If he spends £627 on a holiday, how much will he have left?

$$\begin{array}{r} {}^{8\,13\,1}9\,546 \\ -\ \ 627 \\ \hline 8\,919 \end{array}$$ £8 919

The child should recognise when sums require decomposition, which means 'borrowing' or 'stealing' from the digit on the left. It is better to use the term 'stealing' since the number is never returned.

☆ ## Real life problems

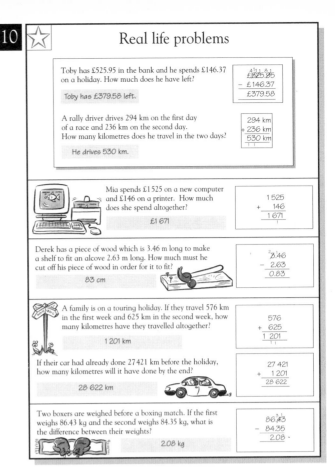

Toby has £525.95 in the bank and he spends £146.37 on a holiday. How much does he have left?

Toby has £379.58 left.

$$\begin{array}{r} {}^{4\,1\,1\ 8\,1}£525.95 \\ -\ £146.37 \\ \hline £379.58 \end{array}$$

A rally driver drives 294 km on the first day of a race and 236 km on the second day. How many kilometres does he travel in the two days?

He drives 530 km.

$$\begin{array}{r} 294\ km \\ +\ 236\ km \\ \hline 530\ km \\ {}^{1} \end{array}$$

Mia spends £1 525 on a new computer and £146 on a printer. How much does she spend altogether?

£1 671

$$\begin{array}{r} 1\,525 \\ +\ \ 146 \\ \hline 1\,671 \\ {}^{1} \end{array}$$

Derek has a piece of wood which is 3.46 m long to make a shelf to fit an alcove 2.63 m long. How much must he cut off his piece of wood in order for it to fit?

83 cm

$$\begin{array}{r} {}^{2}3.46 \\ -\ 2.63 \\ \hline 0.83 \end{array}$$

A family is on a touring holiday. If they travel 576 km in the first week and 625 km in the second week, how many kilometres have they travelled altogether?

1 201 km

$$\begin{array}{r} 576 \\ +\ 625 \\ \hline 1\,201 \\ {}^{1} \end{array}$$

If their car had already done 27 421 km before the holiday, how many kilometres will it have done by the end?

28 622 km

$$\begin{array}{r} 27\,421 \\ +\ \ 1\,201 \\ \hline 28\,622 \end{array}$$

Two boxers are weighed before a boxing match. If the first weighs 86.43 kg and the second weighs 84.35 kg, what is the difference between their weights?

2.08 kg

$$\begin{array}{r} 86.43 \\ -\ 84.35 \\ \hline 2.08\ \cdot \end{array}$$

This page and the following two pages provide an opportunity to apply the skills of addition and subtraction to real life problems, using various units of measurement. If the child is unsure which operation to use, discuss whether the answer will be larger or smaller.

☆ ## Real life problems

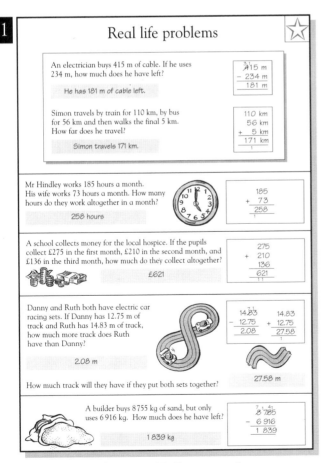

An electrician buys 415 m of cable. If he uses 234 m, how much does he have left?

He has 181 m of cable left.

$$\begin{array}{r} {}^{3\,1}415\ m \\ -\ 234\ m \\ \hline 181\ m \end{array}$$

Simon travels by train for 110 km, by bus for 56 km and then walks the final 5 km. How far does he travel?

Simon travels 171 km.

$$\begin{array}{r} 110\ km \\ 56\ km \\ +\ \ 5\ km \\ \hline 171\ km \\ {}^{1} \end{array}$$

Mr Hindley works 185 hours a month. His wife works 73 hours a month. How many hours do they work altogether in a month?

258 hours

$$\begin{array}{r} 185 \\ +\ \ 73 \\ \hline 258 \\ {}^{1} \end{array}$$

A school collects money for the local hospice. If the pupils collect £275 in the first month, £210 in the second month, and £136 in the third month, how much do they collect altogether?

£621

$$\begin{array}{r} 275 \\ +\ 210 \\ 136 \\ \hline 621 \end{array}$$

Danny and Ruth both have electric car racing sets. If Danny has 12.75 m of track and Ruth has 14.83 m of track, how much more track does Ruth have than Danny?

2.08 m

$$\begin{array}{r} 14.83 \\ -\ 12.75 \\ \hline 2.08 \end{array}$$

How much track will they have if they put both sets together?

27.58 m

$$\begin{array}{r} 14.83 \\ +\ 12.75 \\ \hline 27.58 \\ {}^{1} \end{array}$$

A builder buys 8 755 kg of sand, but only uses 6 916 kg. How much does he have left?

1 839 kg

$$\begin{array}{r} {}^{7\ 1\ 41}8\,755 \\ -\ 6\,916 \\ \hline 1\,839 \end{array}$$

See the notes for page 10. Point out that an answer that will be larger will require addition, while one that will be smaller will require subtraction.

☆ ## Real life problems

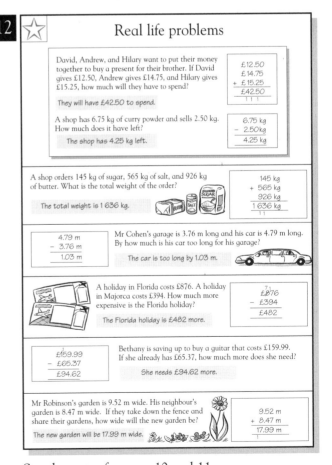

David, Andrew, and Hilary want to put their money together to buy a present for their brother. If David gives £12.50, Andrew gives £14.75, and Hilary gives £15.25, how much will they have to spend?

They will have £42.50 to spend.

$$\begin{array}{r} £12.50 \\ £14.75 \\ +\ £15.25 \\ \hline £42.50 \\ {}^{1\,1\,1} \end{array}$$

A shop has 6.75 kg of curry powder and sells 2.50 kg. How much does it have left?

The shop has 4.25 kg left.

$$\begin{array}{r} 6.75\ kg \\ -\ 2.50\ kg \\ \hline 4.25\ kg \end{array}$$

A shop orders 145 kg of sugar, 565 kg of salt, and 926 kg of butter. What is the total weight of the order?

The total weight is 1 636 kg.

$$\begin{array}{r} 145\ kg \\ +\ 565\ kg \\ 926\ kg \\ \hline 1\,636\ kg \\ {}^{1\,1} \end{array}$$

Mr Cohen's garage is 3.76 m long and his car is 4.79 m long. By how much is his car too long for his garage?

The car is too long by 1.03 m.

$$\begin{array}{r} 4.79\ m \\ -\ 3.76\ m \\ \hline 1.03\ m \end{array}$$

A holiday in Florida costs £876. A holiday in Majorca costs £394. How much more expensive is the Florida holiday?

The Florida holiday is £482 more.

$$\begin{array}{r} {}^{7\,1}£876 \\ -\ £394 \\ \hline £482 \end{array}$$

Bethany is saving up to buy a guitar that costs £159.99. If she already has £65.37, how much more does she need?

She needs £94.62 more.

$$\begin{array}{r} £159.99 \\ -\ £65.37 \\ \hline £94.62 \end{array}$$

Mr Robinson's garden is 9.52 m wide. His neighbour's garden is 8.47 m wide. If they take down the fence and share their gardens, how wide will the new garden be?

The new garden will be 17.99 m wide.

$$\begin{array}{r} 9.52\ m \\ +\ 8.47\ m \\ \hline 17.99\ m \end{array}$$

See the notes for page 10 and 11.

Decimal addition

Write in the answers to these sums.

47.15	43.99
+19.36	+12.76
66.51	56.75

Write the answer to each sum.

53.72	84.17	29.36	23.56	62.49
+77.92	+68.21	+66.84	+79.14	+18.75
131.64	152.38	96.20	102.70	81.24

35.67	29.88	67.39	49.32	27.22
+12.99	+43.02	+81.70	+14.95	+38.84
48.66	72.90	149.09	64.27	66.06

Write the answer to each sum.

76.30	44.29	81.97	29.86	68.25
+22.97	+11.04	+69.14	+76.33	+84.36
99.27	55.33	151.11	106.19	152.61

83.90	45.83	52.17	84.93	72.83
+30.24	+45.71	+90.21	+29.37	+41.16
114.14	91.54	142.38	114.30	113.99

Write the answer to each sum.

37.89 + 82.15 = 120.04   32.44 + 21.88 = 54.32   37.19 + 28.24 = 65.43

68.67 + 29.82 = 98.49   21.99 + 79.32 = 101.31   52.45 + 34.58 = 87.03

84.77 + 39.12 = 123.89   63.84 + 29.81 = 93.65   34.43 + 25.64 = 60.07

33.97 + 24.62 = 58.59   76.39 + 43.78 = 120.17   52.38 + 38.43 = 90.81

This page and the next page should follow on from earlier addition work. On these two pages the child is dealing with two decimal places. The most likely mistakes will be errors involving carrying or, in the third section, where they are working horizontally.

Decimal addition

Write the answer to each sum.

296.48	173.05
+ 131.74	+ 269.23
428.22	442.28

Write the answer to each sum.

491.83	964.71	302.04	306.25
+ 137.84	+ 321.26	+ 204.99	+ 844.24
629.67	1285.97	507.03	1150.49

471.93	842.01	675.82	137.82
+ 755.26	+ 711.84	+105.23	+ 399.71
1227.19	1553.85	781.05	537.53

465.24	178.93	184.74	443.27
+ 605.27	+ 599.41	+ 372.81	+ 705.99
1070.51	778.34	557.55	1149.26

563.23	703.95	825.36	529.33
+ 413.98	+ 685.11	+ 249.85	+ 482.56
977.21	1389.06	1075.21	1011.89

Write the answer to each sum.

421.79 + 136.25 = 558.04   192.31 + 241.73 = 434.04

558.32 + 137.94 = 696.26   501.84 + 361.93 = 863.77

227.66 + 142.07 = 369.73   275.31 + 239.33 = 514.64

153.31 + 189.02 = 342.33   491.44 + 105.37 = 596.81

253.71 + 562.41 = 816.12   829.25 + 163.74 = 992.99

Look out for errors when the child is working horizontally, adding digits with different place values. Less confident children may need to be reassured when carrying across the decimal point

Decimal subtraction

Write the answer to each sum.

59.76	57.18
− 21.47	− 22.09
38.29	35.09

Write the answer to each sum.

64.92	64.21	73.71	92.63
− 26.35	− 16.02	− 19.24	− 67.14
38.57	48.19	54.47	25.49

45.76	73.52	98.98	53.58
− 16.18	− 39.27	− 39.19	− 14.39
29.58	34.25	59.79	39.19

94.87	21.74	62.35	81.94
− 65.28	− 12.15	− 13.16	− 28.15
29.59	9.59	49.19	53.79

62.95	81.42	48.52	61.55
− 33.37	− 25.04	− 14.49	− 13.26
29.58	56.38	34.03	48.29

Write the answer to each sum.

51.52 − 12.13 = 39.39   72.41 − 23.18 = 49.23

91.91 − 22.22 = 69.69   53.84 − 19.65 = 34.19

41.82 − 18.13 = 23.69   51.61 − 23.14 = 28.47

83.91 − 14.73 = 69.18   64.65 − 37.26 = 27.39

53.21 − 35.12 = 18.09   77.31 − 28.15 = 49.16

On this page and the next two pages, the most likely errors will result from a failure to use decomposition where necessary (see notes to pages 8 and 9). Watch out for misalignment when the child is working on horizontal subtractions.

Decimal subtraction

Write the answer to each sum.

68.17	39.24
− 11.43	− 13.51
56.74	25.73

Write the answer to each sum.

87.23	93.15	66.37	85.15
− 24.41	− 31.35	− 21.93	− 26.32
62.82	63.80	44.44	58.83

72.28	63.14	99.22	62.19
− 21.36	− 32.41	− 33.70	− 29.34
50.92	30.73	65.52	32.85

77.36	53.49	68.25	41.14
− 24.42	− 27.66	− 31.51	− 13.20
52.94	27.83	36.74	27.94

82.35	63.29	53.64	35.61
− 23.41	− 15.36	− 23.72	− 26.19
58.94	47.93	29.92	9.42

Write the answer to each sum.

63.46 − 24.51 = 38.95   92.19 − 63.28 = 28.91

91.35 − 33.42 = 57.93   41.24 − 14.30 = 26.94

52.25 − 23.42 = 28.83   72.63 − 53.71 = 18.92

92.84 − 23.93 = 68.91   61.16 − 24.42 = 36.74

81.81 − 55.90 = 25.91   94.31 − 27.40 = 66.91

As for the previous page, the child must use decomposition where necessary. Misalignment in horizontal subtractions may result in digits of different place values being subtracted.

Multiplying larger numbers by units ☆

Write the answer to each sum.

529	1273
× 4	× 5
2116	6365
₁₃	₁ ₃ ₁

Write the answer to each sum.

724	831	126	455
× 2	× 3	× 3	× 4
1448	2493	378	1820
		₁	₂ ₂

161	282	349	253
× 4	× 5	× 5	× 6
644	1410	1745	1518
₂	₄₁	₂ ₄	₃₁

328	465	105	562
× 6	× 6	× 4	× 4
1968	2790	420	2248
₁ ₄	₃₃		₂

Write the answer to each sum.

4261	1582	3612	4284
× 3	× 3	× 4	× 4
12783	4746	14448	17136
₁	₁₂	₂	₁ ₃₁

5907	1263	1303	1467
× 5	× 5	× 6	× 6
29535	6315	7818	8802
₄ ₃	₁ ₃₁	₁ ₁	₂ ₄₄

6521	8436	1599	3761
× 6	× 6	× 6	× 6
39126	50616	9594	22566
₃₁	₂ ₂₃	₃ ₅₅	₄₃

5837	6394	8124	3914
× 4	× 5	× 6	× 6
23348	31970	48744	23484
₃ ₁₂	₁ ₄₂	₁ ₂	₅ ₂

Make sure that the child understands the convention of multiplication sums, i.e. multiply units first and work left. Problems on this page will generally highlight gaps in knowledge of multiplication tables 2, 3, 4, 5, and 6. Make sure that the child is carrying when necessary.

☆ Multiplying larger numbers by units

Write the answer to each sum.

417	2185
× 7	× 9
2919	19665
₁₄	₁ ₇ ₄

Write the answer to each sum.

419	604	715	327
× 7	× 7	× 8	× 7
2933	4228	5720	2289
₁₆	₂	₁₄	₁₄

425	171	682	246
× 8	× 9	× 8	× 8
3400	1539	5456	1968
₂₄	₆	₆₁	₃₄

436	999	319	581
× 8	× 9	× 9	× 9
3488	8991	2871	5229
₂₄	₈₈	₁₈	₇

Work out the answer to each sum.

4331	2816	1439	2617
× 7	× 7	× 8	× 8
30317	19712	11512	20936
₂ ₂	₅ ₁₄	₃ ₃₇	₄ ₁₅

3104	4022	3212	2591
× 8	× 8	× 9	× 9
24832	32176	28908	23319
₃	₁₁	₁ ₁₁	₅ ₈

1710	3002	2468	1514
× 9	× 8	× 7	× 8
15390	24016	17276	12112
₆	₁	₃ ₄₅	₄ ₁₃

4624	2993	3894	4361
× 7	× 8	× 8	× 9
32368	23944	31152	39249
₄ ₁₂	₇ ₇₂	₇ ₇₃	₃ ₅

Any problems encountered on this page will be similar to those of the previous page. Gaps in the child's knowledge of multiplication tables 7, 8, and 9 will be highlighted here.

Real life problems with multiplying ☆

There are 157 apples in a box. How many will there be in three boxes?

157
× 3
471
₁ ₂

471 apples

A stamp album can hold 550 stamps. How many stamps will 5 albums hold?

550
× 5
2750
₂

2750 stamps

A train can take 425 passengers. How many can it take in four journeys?

425
× 4
1700
₁ ₂

1700 passengers

Mr Jenkins puts £256 a month into the bank. How much will he have put in after six months?

256
× 6
1536
₃₃

£1536

A theatre can seat 5 524 people. If a play runs for 7 days, what is the maximum number of people who will be able to see it?

5524
× 7
38668
₃ ₁ ₂

38 668 people

A car costs £9956. How much will it cost a company to buy nine cars for its salesmen?

9956
× 9
89604
₈ ₆₅

£89 604

A new window for a house costs £435. How much will it cost to fit 8 windows of the same size?

435
× 8
3480
₂ ₄ ₀

£3 480

An aeroplane flies at a steady speed of 550 kph. How far will it travel in 7 hours?

550
× 7
3850
₃

3 850 km

This page provides an opportunity for the child to apply their skills of multiplication to real life problems. As with the previous multiplication work, gaps in the child's knowledge of multiplication facts will be highlighted here.

☆ Real life problems with percentages

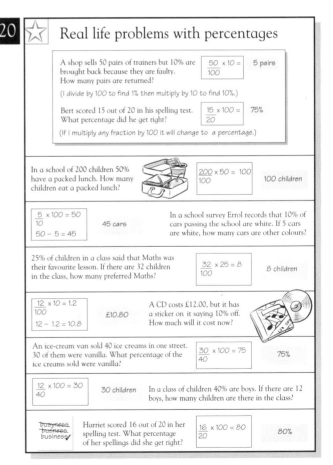

A shop sells 50 pairs of trainers but 10% are brought back because they are faulty. How many pairs are returned?

$\frac{50 \times 10}{100} =$ 5 pairs

(I divide by 100 to find 1% then multiply by 10 to find 10%.)

Bert scored 15 out of 20 in his spelling test. What percentage did he get right?

$\frac{15 \times 100}{20} =$ 75%

(If I multiply any fraction by 100 it will change to a percentage.)

In a school of 200 children 50% have a packed lunch. How many children eat a packed lunch?

$\frac{200 \times 50}{100} = 100$ 100 children

$\frac{5 \times 100}{10} = 50$
$50 - 5 = 45$ 45 cars

In a school survey Errol records that 10% of cars passing the school are white. If 5 cars are white, how many cars are other colours?

25% of children in a class said that Maths was their favourite lesson. If there are 32 children in the class, how many preferred Maths?

$\frac{32 \times 25}{100} = 8$ 8 children

$\frac{12 \times 10}{100} = 1.2$
$12 - 1.2 = 10.8$ £10.80

A CD costs £12.00, but it has a sticker on it saying 10% off. How much will it cost now?

An ice-cream van sold 40 ice creams in one street. 30 of them were vanilla. What percentage of the ice creams sold were vanilla?

$\frac{30 \times 100}{40} = 75$ 75%

$\frac{12 \times 100}{40} = 30$ 30 children

In a class of children 40% are boys. If there are 12 boys, how many children are there in the class?

Harriet scored 16 out of 20 in her spelling test. What percentage of her spellings did she get right?

$\frac{16 \times 100}{20} = 80$ 80%

This page gives the child an opportunity to practise simple percentages applied to real life situations. Finding a percentage of a given total should be fairly straightforward, but where a percentage is given and the total is required, some discussion may be needed.

Converting units ☆

Convert 25 centimetres to millimetres.   Convert 200p to pounds.

$25 \times 10 =$ 250 mm $200 \div 100 =$ £2

Convert these centimetres to millimetres.

40 cm	400 mm	15 cm	150 mm	9 cm	90 mm
12 cm	120 mm	34 cm	340 mm	62 cm	620 mm
43 cm	430 mm	96 cm	960 mm	105 cm	1050 mm
92 cm	920 mm	20 cm	200 mm	426 cm	4260 mm

Convert these millimetres to centimetres.

30 mm	3 cm	100 mm	10 cm	120 mm	12 cm
60 mm	6 cm	90 mm	9 cm	200 mm	20 cm
130 mm	13 cm	10 mm	1 cm	400 mm	40 cm

Convert these pounds to pence.

£35	3500p	£600	60 000p	£15	1500p
£12	1200p	£36	3600p	£95	9500p
£72	7200p	£4	400p	£250	25 000p

Convert these pence to pounds.

450p	£4.50	900p	£9.00	6000p	£60.00
250p	£2.50	400p	£4.00	150p	£1.50
100p	£1.00	300p	£3.00	750p	£7.50

This page will highlight any problems with the relationship between millimetres and centimetres, and pounds and pence. Use a ruler or money to explain. Watch out for answers such as £7.5. Remind the child that, with money, we use zero in the units column.

Converting units

Convert 300 centimetres to metres.   Convert 4 kilometres to metres.

$300 \div 100 =$ 3 m $4 \times 1000 =$ 4 000 m

Convert these centimetres to metres.

500 cm	5 m	900 cm	9 m	400 cm	4 m
8 000 cm	80 m	3 000 cm	30 m	4 000 cm	40 m
9 800 cm	98 m	8 300 cm	83 m	6 200 cm	62 m
36 800 cm	368 m	94 200 cm	942 m	73 500 cm	735 m

Convert these metres to centimetres.

47 m	4 700 cm	29 m	2 900 cm	84 m	8 400 cm
69 m	6 900 cm	24 m	2 400 cm	38 m	3 800 cm
146 m	14 600 cm	237 m	23 700 cm	921 m	92 100 cm

Convert these metres to kilometres.

5 000 m	5 km	6 000 m	6 km	9 000 m	9 km
15 000 m	15 km	27 000 m	27 km	71 000 m	71 km
19 000 m	19 km	86 000 m	86 km	42 000 m	42 km

Convert these kilometres to metres.

7 km	7 000 m	9 km	9 000 m	4 km	4 000 m
23 km	23 000 m	46 km	46 000 m	87 km	87 000 m
12 km	12 000 m	96 km	96 000 m	39 km	39 000 m

As with the previous page, check that the child understands the relationship between centimetres and metres, and metres and kilometres. If they are secure in this understanding, this should be a straightforward page of multiplying and dividing by 100 and 1 000.

Area of rectangles and squares ☆

Find the area of this rectangle.
To find the area of a rectangle or square we multiply length (l) by width (w).
Area = 800 cm²

(w) 25 cm   (l) 32 cm

```
   32
 × 25
 ----
  160
 +640
 ----
  800 cm²
    1
```

Find the area of these rectangles and squares.
You will need to do your working on a separate sheet.

42 cm / 21 cm → 882 cm²

84 cm / 84 cm → 7056 cm²

95 m / 36 m → 3420 m²

41 m / 87 m → 3567 m²

68 mm / 49 mm → 3332 mm²

77 mm / 83 mm → 6391 mm²

99 cm / 99 cm → 9801 cm²

39 cm / 85 cm → 3315 cm²

69 cm / 83 cm → 5727 cm²

For the exercises on this page, the child needs to multiply the two sides together to arrive at the area. If any answers are wrong, check the long multiplication and, if necessary, revise the method. The child may confuse area and perimeter, and add the sides together.

Perimeter of shapes

Find the perimeter of this rectangle.
To find the perimeter of a rectangle or square we add the two lengths and the two widths together.

12.4 cm   27.3 cm

```
  27.3 cm
  27.3 cm
  12.4 cm
+ 12.4 cm
 --------
  79.4 cm
   11
```
79.4 cm

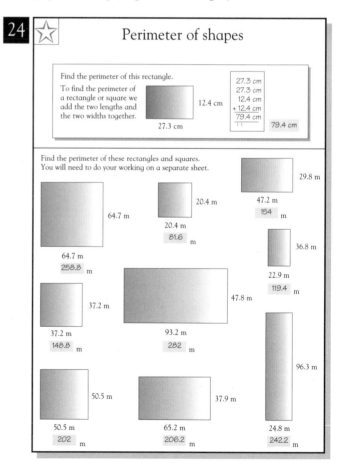

Find the perimeter of these rectangles and squares.
You will need to do your working on a separate sheet.

64.7 m / 64.7 m → 258.8 m

20.4 m / 20.4 m → 81.6 m

29.8 m / 47.2 m → 154 m

37.2 m / 37.2 m → 148.8 m

47.8 m / 93.2 m → 282 m

36.8 m / 22.9 m → 119.4 m

50.5 m / 50.5 m → 202 m

37.9 m / 65.2 m → 206.2 m

96.3 m / 24.8 m → 242.2 m

On this page and the next page, the most likely problem will be confusion with the area work done on the previous page. Remind the child to add the four sides together.

Find the perimeter of these rectangles and squares.
You will need to do your working on a separate sheet.

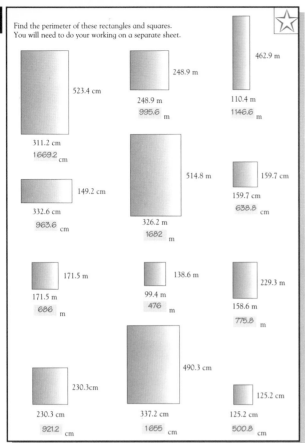

462.9 m

248.9 m

248.9 m
995.6 m

110.4 m
1146.6 m

523.4 cm

311.2 cm
1669.2 cm

514.8 m

159.7 cm

149.2 cm

332.6 cm
963.6 cm

326.2 m
1682 m

159.7 cm
638.8 cm

171.5 m
171.5 m
686 m

138.6 m
99.4 m
476 m

229.3 m
158.6 m
775.8 m

490.3 cm

230.3cm
230.3 cm
921.2 cm

337.2 cm
1655 cm

125.2 cm
125.2 cm
500.8 cm

These exercises follow on from the previous page.
If the child is confident, it may be appropriate to
discuss an alternative method of finding the
perimeter of a square, i.e. multiplying one side by four.

Speed problems

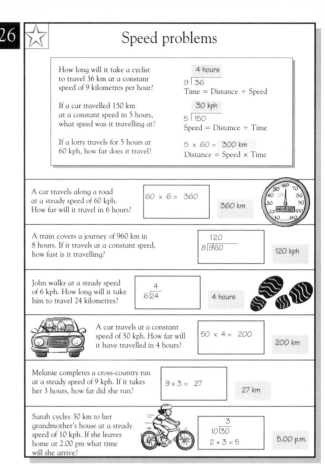

How long will it take a cyclist
to travel 36 km at a constant
speed of 9 kilometres per hour?

4 hours
9 ⟌ 36
Time = Distance ÷ Speed

If a car travelled 150 km
at a constant speed in 5 hours,
what speed was it travelling at?

30 kph
5 ⟌ 150
Speed = Distance ÷ Time

If a lorry travels for 5 hours at
60 kph, how far does it travel?

5 × 60 = 300 km
Distance = Speed × Time

A car travels along a road
at a steady speed of 60 kph.
How far will it travel in 6 hours?

60 × 6 = 360   360 km

A train covers a journey of 960 km in
8 hours. If it travels at a constant speed,
how fast is it travelling?

120
8 ⟌ 960   120 kph

John walks at a steady speed
of 6 kph. How long will it take
him to travel 24 kilometres?

4
6 ⟌ 24   4 hours

A car travels at a constant
speed of 50 kph. How far will
it have travelled in 4 hours?

50 × 4 = 200   200 km

Melanie completes a cross-country run
at a steady speed of 9 kph. If it takes
her 3 hours, how far did she run?

9 × 3 = 27   27 km

Sarah cycles 30 km to her
grandmother's house at a steady
speed of 10 kph. If she leaves
home at 2.00 pm what time
will she arrive?

3
10 ⟌ 30
2 + 3 = 5   5.00 p.m.

If the child experiences difficulty on this page, ask
them what they need to find, i.e. speed, distance, or
time, and refer to the formula necessary to find this.
Encourage the child to develop simple examples
which will help them to remember the formulae.

Conversion table

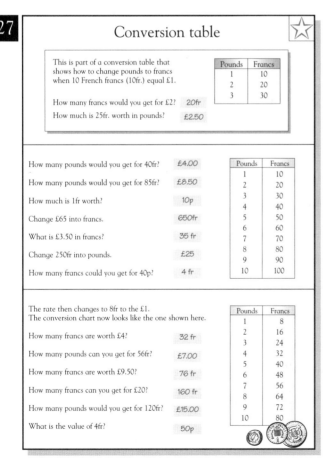

This is part of a conversion table that
shows how to change pounds to francs
when 10 French francs (10fr.) equal £1.

Pounds	Francs
1	10
2	20
3	30

How many francs would you get for £2?   20fr

How much is 25fr. worth in pounds?   £2.50

How many pounds would you get for 40fr?   £4.00

How many pounds would you get for 85fr?   £8.50

How much is 1fr worth?   10p

Change £65 into francs.   650fr

What is £3.50 in francs?   35 fr

Change 250fr into pounds.   £25

How many francs could you get for 40p?   4 fr

Pounds	Francs
1	10
2	20
3	30
4	40
5	50
6	60
7	70
8	80
9	90
10	100

The rate then changes to 8fr to the £1.
The conversion chart now looks like the one shown here.

How many francs are worth £4?   32 fr

How many pounds can you get for 56fr?   £7.00

How many francs are worth £9.50?   76 fr

How many francs can you get for £20?   160 fr

How many pounds would you get for 120fr?   £15.00

What is the value of 4fr?   50p

Pounds	Francs
1	8
2	16
3	24
4	32
5	40
6	48
7	56
8	64
9	72
10	80

Most of the questions on this page require reading off
from a conversion chart. Errors may occur when not
reading across accurately. Where the questions involve
amounts not on the chart, the child may need extra
help. Check the right chart is used for the second part.

Interpreting pie charts

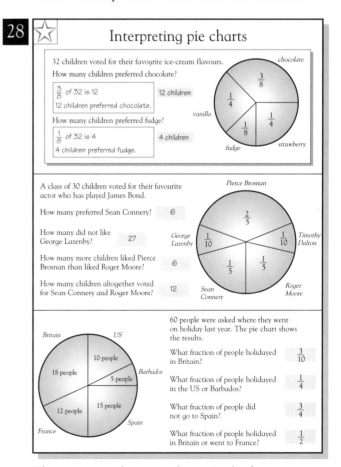

32 children voted for their favourite ice-cream flavours.
How many children preferred chocolate?

3/8 of 32 is 12
12 children preferred chocolate.   12 children

chocolate
3/8
1/4
1/4
1/8
vanilla
fudge   strawberry

How many children preferred fudge?

1/8 of 32 is 4
4 children preferred fudge.   4 children

A class of 30 children voted for their favourite
actor who has played James Bond.

How many preferred Sean Connery?   6

How many did not like
George Lazenby?   27

How many more children liked Pierce
Brosnan than liked Roger Moore?   6

How many children altogether voted
for Sean Connery and Roger Moore?   12

Pierce Brosnan
2/5
George Lazenby 1/10
1/10 Timothy Dalton
1/5
1/5
Sean Connery
Roger Moore

60 people were asked where they went
on holiday last year. The pie chart shows
the results.

What fraction of people holidayed
in Britain?   3/10

What fraction of people holidayed
in the US or Barbados?   1/4

What fraction of people did
not go to Spain?   3/4

What fraction of people holidayed
in Britain or went to France?   1/2

Britain   US
10 people
18 people   Barbados
5 people
12 people   15 people
France   Spain

This page introduces pie charts. In the first section
the child is required to find fractions of an amount.
If unsure, remind the child to divide the total by the
denominator and multiply by the numerator. The most
likely errors will come from misreading the question.

Probability scale 0 to 1

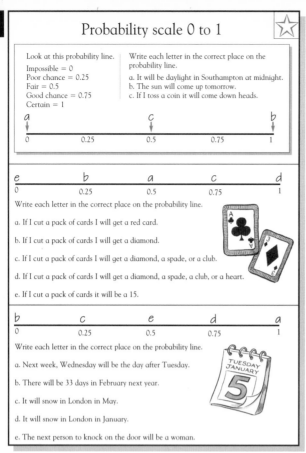

Look at this probability line.

Impossible = 0
Poor chance = 0.25
Fair = 0.5
Good chance = 0.75
Certain = 1

Write each letter in the correct place on the probability line.

a. It will be daylight in Southampton at midnight.
b. The sun will come up tomorrow.
c. If I toss a coin it will come down heads.

Write each letter in the correct place on the probability line.

a. If I cut a pack of cards I will get a red card.

b. If I cut a pack of cards I will get a diamond.

c. If I cut a pack of cards I will get a diamond, a spade, or a club.

d. If I cut a pack of cards I will get a diamond, a spade, a club, or a heart.

e. If I cut a pack of cards it will be a 15.

Write each letter in the correct place on the probability line.

a. Next week, Wednesday will be the day after Tuesday.

b. There will be 33 days in February next year.

c. It will snow in London in May.

d. It will snow in London in January.

e. The next person to knock on the door will be a woman.

The first section presupposes a knowledge of the suits of a pack of cards. If the child is unfamiliar with cards some discussion will be necessary. In the second section the examples have been chosen to fall fairly firmly into the categories listed on the probability line.

Likely outcomes

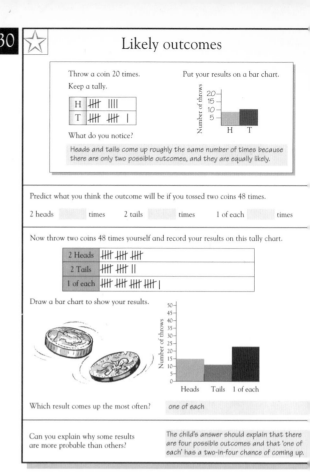

Throw a coin 20 times.
Keep a tally.

| H | ⅢⅢ ⅢⅠ |
| T | ⅢⅢ ⅢⅢ Ⅰ |

What do you notice?

Put your results on a bar chart.

Heads and tails come up roughly the same number of times because there are only two possible outcomes, and they are equally likely.

Predict what you think the outcome will be if you tossed two coins 48 times.

2 heads _____ times   2 tails _____ times   1 of each _____ times

Now throw two coins 48 times yourself and record your results on this tally chart.

2 Heads	ⅢⅢ ⅢⅢ ⅢⅢ
2 Tails	ⅢⅢ ⅢⅢ ⅠⅠ
1 of each	ⅢⅢ ⅢⅢ ⅢⅢ ⅢⅢ Ⅰ

Draw a bar chart to show your results.

Which result comes up the most often?   one of each

Can you explain why some results are more probable than others?

The child's answer should explain that there are four possible outcomes and that 'one of each' has a two-in-four chance of coming up.

The child's prediction in the first question may be considerably different from the result. Once the work is done check that the child can use the experience to improve their understanding of likely outcomes. The tally chart may differ from the one shown here.

Naming quadrilaterals

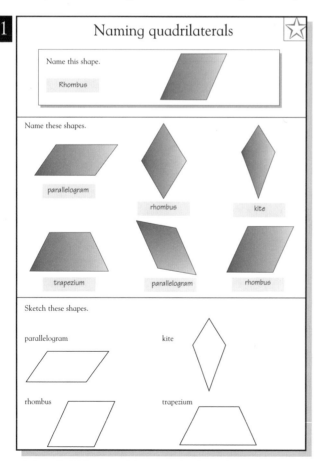

Name this shape.

Rhombus

Name these shapes.

parallelogram

rhombus

kite

trapezium

parallelogram

rhombus

Sketch these shapes.

parallelogram   kite

rhombus   trapezium

If the child has problems with identifying these shapes, it may be necessary to provide some more examples for identification.

3D planes of symmetry

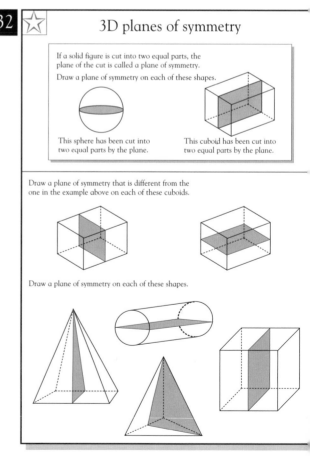

If a solid figure is cut into two equal parts, the plane of the cut is called a plane of symmetry.

Draw a plane of symmetry on each of these shapes.

This sphere has been cut into two equal parts by the plane.

This cuboid has been cut into two equal parts by the plane.

Draw a plane of symmetry that is different from the one in the example above on each of these cuboids.

Draw a plane of symmetry on each of these shapes.

There are several different answers for some of the shapes. The ones shown above are suggested planes of symmetry.

Multiplying larger numbers by units

Write the answer to each sum.

```
   724          831          126          455
 ×   2        ×   3        ×   3        ×   4
 ‾‾‾‾‾        ‾‾‾‾‾        ‾‾‾‾‾        ‾‾‾‾‾
 _____        _____        _____        _____


   161          282          349          253
 ×   4        ×   5        ×   5        ×   6
 ‾‾‾‾‾        ‾‾‾‾‾        ‾‾‾‾‾        ‾‾‾‾‾
 _____        _____        _____        _____


   328          465          105          562
 ×   6        ×   6        ×   4        ×   4
 ‾‾‾‾‾        ‾‾‾‾‾        ‾‾‾‾‾        ‾‾‾‾‾
 _____        _____        _____        _____
```

Write the answer to each sum.

```
  4261         1582         3612         4284
 ×    3        ×    3        ×    4        ×    4
 ‾‾‾‾‾‾        ‾‾‾‾‾‾        ‾‾‾‾‾‾        ‾‾‾‾‾‾
 _____        _____        _____        _____


  5907         1263         1303         1467
 ×    5        ×    5        ×    6        ×    6
 ‾‾‾‾‾‾        ‾‾‾‾‾‾        ‾‾‾‾‾‾        ‾‾‾‾‾‾
 _____        _____        _____        _____


  6521         8436         1599         3761
 ×    6        ×    6        ×    6        ×    6
 ‾‾‾‾‾‾        ‾‾‾‾‾‾        ‾‾‾‾‾‾        ‾‾‾‾‾‾
 _____        _____        _____        _____


  5837         6394         8124         3914
 ×    4        ×    5        ×    6        ×    6
 ‾‾‾‾‾‾        ‾‾‾‾‾‾        ‾‾‾‾‾‾        ‾‾‾‾‾‾
 _____        _____        _____        _____
```

Multiplying larger numbers by units

Write the answer to each sum.

$$
\begin{array}{r}
417 \\
\times \quad 7 \\
\hline
2\,919 \\
\hline
{\scriptstyle 1\,4}
\end{array}
\qquad
\begin{array}{r}
2\,185 \\
\times \quad 9 \\
\hline
19\,665 \\
\hline
{\scriptstyle 1\,7\,4}
\end{array}
$$

Write the answer to each sum.

$$
\begin{array}{r}
419 \\
\times \ 7 \\
\hline
\end{array}
\qquad
\begin{array}{r}
604 \\
\times \ 7 \\
\hline
\end{array}
\qquad
\begin{array}{r}
715 \\
\times \ 8 \\
\hline
\end{array}
\qquad
\begin{array}{r}
327 \\
\times \ 7 \\
\hline
\end{array}
$$

$$
\begin{array}{r}
425 \\
\times \ 8 \\
\hline
\end{array}
\qquad
\begin{array}{r}
171 \\
\times \ 9 \\
\hline
\end{array}
\qquad
\begin{array}{r}
682 \\
\times \ 8 \\
\hline
\end{array}
\qquad
\begin{array}{r}
246 \\
\times \ 8 \\
\hline
\end{array}
$$

$$
\begin{array}{r}
436 \\
\times \ 8 \\
\hline
\end{array}
\qquad
\begin{array}{r}
999 \\
\times \ 9 \\
\hline
\end{array}
\qquad
\begin{array}{r}
319 \\
\times \ 9 \\
\hline
\end{array}
\qquad
\begin{array}{r}
581 \\
\times \ 9 \\
\hline
\end{array}
$$

Work out the answer to each sum.

$$
\begin{array}{r}
4\,331 \\
\times \quad 7 \\
\hline
\end{array}
\qquad
\begin{array}{r}
2\,816 \\
\times \quad 7 \\
\hline
\end{array}
\qquad
\begin{array}{r}
1\,439 \\
\times \quad 8 \\
\hline
\end{array}
\qquad
\begin{array}{r}
2\,617 \\
\times \quad 8 \\
\hline
\end{array}
$$

$$
\begin{array}{r}
3\,104 \\
\times \quad 8 \\
\hline
\end{array}
\qquad
\begin{array}{r}
4\,022 \\
\times \quad 8 \\
\hline
\end{array}
\qquad
\begin{array}{r}
3\,212 \\
\times \quad 9 \\
\hline
\end{array}
\qquad
\begin{array}{r}
2\,591 \\
\times \quad 9 \\
\hline
\end{array}
$$

$$
\begin{array}{r}
1\,710 \\
\times \quad 9 \\
\hline
\end{array}
\qquad
\begin{array}{r}
3\,002 \\
\times \quad 8 \\
\hline
\end{array}
\qquad
\begin{array}{r}
2\,468 \\
\times \quad 7 \\
\hline
\end{array}
\qquad
\begin{array}{r}
1\,514 \\
\times \quad 8 \\
\hline
\end{array}
$$

$$
\begin{array}{r}
4\,624 \\
\times \quad 7 \\
\hline
\end{array}
\qquad
\begin{array}{r}
2\,993 \\
\times \quad 8 \\
\hline
\end{array}
\qquad
\begin{array}{r}
3\,894 \\
\times \quad 8 \\
\hline
\end{array}
\qquad
\begin{array}{r}
4\,361 \\
\times \quad 9 \\
\hline
\end{array}
$$

Real life problems with multiplying

There are 157 apples in a box.
How many will there be in three boxes?

471 apples

```
  157
×   3
─────
  471
   12
```

A stamp album can hold 550 stamps.
How many stamps will 5 albums hold?

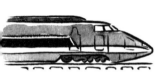

A train can take 425 passengers.
How many can it take in four journeys?

Mr Jenkins puts £256 a month into the bank.
How much will he have put in after six months?

A theatre can seat 5 524 people. If a play runs for 7 days, what is the maximum number of people who will be able to see it?

A car costs £9956. How much will it cost a company to buy nine cars for its salesmen?

A new window for a house costs £435. How much will it cost to fit 8 windows of the same size?

An aeroplane flies at a steady speed of 550 kph.
How far will it travel in 7 hours?

Real life problems with percentages

A shop sells 50 pairs of trainers but 10% are brought back because they are faulty.
How many pairs are returned?

$$\frac{50}{100} \times 10 =$$ 5 pairs

(I divide by 100 to find 1% then multiply by 10 to find 10%.)

Bert scored 15 out of 20 in his spelling test. What percentage did he get right?

$$\frac{15}{20} \times 100 =$$ 75%

(If I multiply any fraction by 100 it will change to a percentage.)

In a school of 200 children 50% have a packed lunch. How many children eat a packed lunch?

In a school survey Errol records that 10% of cars passing the school are white. If 5 cars are white, how many cars are other colours?

25% of children in a class said that Maths was their favourite lesson. If there are 32 children in the class, how many preferred Maths?

A CD costs £12.00, but it has a sticker on it saying 10% off. How much will it cost now?

An ice-cream van sold 40 ice creams in one street. 30 of them were vanilla. What percentage of the ice creams sold were vanilla?

In a class of children 40% are boys. If there are 12 boys, how many children are there in the class?

busyness
busness
business ✓

Harriet scored 16 out of 20 in her spelling test. What percentage of her spellings did she get right?

20

Converting units

Convert 25 centimetres to millimetres.   Convert 200p to pounds.

$25 \times 10 =$ 250 mm $200 \div 100 =$ £2

Convert these centimetres to millimetres.

40 cm	15 cm	9 cm
12 cm	34 cm	62 cm
43 cm	96 cm	105 cm
92 cm	20 cm	426 cm

Convert these millimetres to centimetres.

30 mm	100 mm	120 mm
60 mm	90 mm	200 mm
130 mm	10 mm	400 mm

Convert these pounds to pence.

£35	£600	£15
£12	£36	£95
£72	£4	£250

Convert these pence to pounds.

450p	900p	6 000p
250p	400p	150p
100p	300p	750p

Converting units

Convert 300 centimetres to metres.   Convert 4 kilometres to metres.

$300 \div 100 =$ 3 m $4 \times 1000 =$ 4000 m

Convert these centimetres to metres.

500 cm	900 cm	400 cm
8000 cm	3000 cm	4000 cm
9800 cm	8300 cm	6200 cm
36800 cm	94200 cm	73500 cm

Convert these metres to centimetres.

47 m	29 m	84 m
69 m	24 m	38 m
146 m	237 m	921 m

Convert these metres to kilometres.

5000 m	6000 m	9000 m
15000 m	27000 m	71000 m
19000 m	86000 m	42000 m

Convert these kilometres to metres.

7 km	9 km	4 km
23 km	46 km	87 km
12 km	96 km	39 km

Area of rectangles and squares

Find the area of this rectangle.

To find the area of a rectangle or square we multiply length (l) by width (w).

Area = 800 cm²

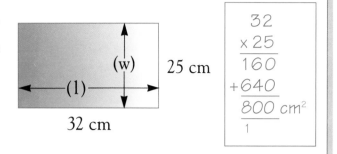

25 cm

32 cm

```
  32
x 25
─────
 160
+640
─────
 800 cm²
   1
```

Find the area of these rectangles and squares.
You will need to do your working on a separate sheet.

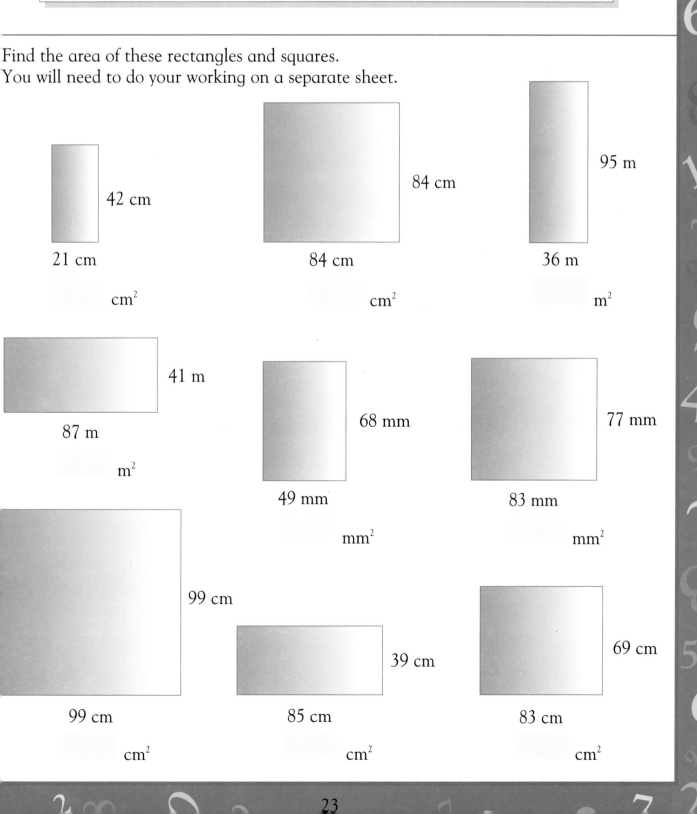

42 cm

21 cm

_____ cm²

84 cm

84 cm

_____ cm²

95 m

36 m

_____ m²

41 m

87 m

_____ m²

68 mm

49 mm

_____ mm²

77 mm

83 mm

_____ mm²

99 cm

99 cm

_____ cm²

39 cm

85 cm

_____ cm²

69 cm

83 cm

_____ cm²

Perimeter of shapes

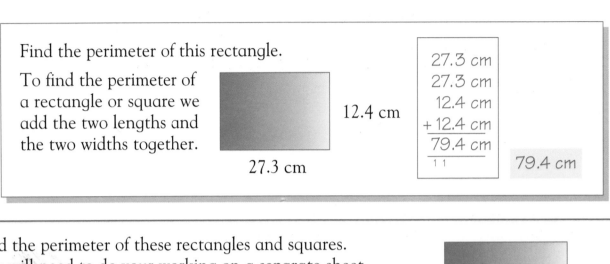

Find the perimeter of this rectangle.

To find the perimeter of a rectangle or square we add the two lengths and the two widths together.

12.4 cm

27.3 cm

```
  27.3 cm
  27.3 cm
  12.4 cm
+ 12.4 cm
  79.4 cm
  1 1
```

79.4 cm

Find the perimeter of these rectangles and squares.
You will need to do your working on a separate sheet.

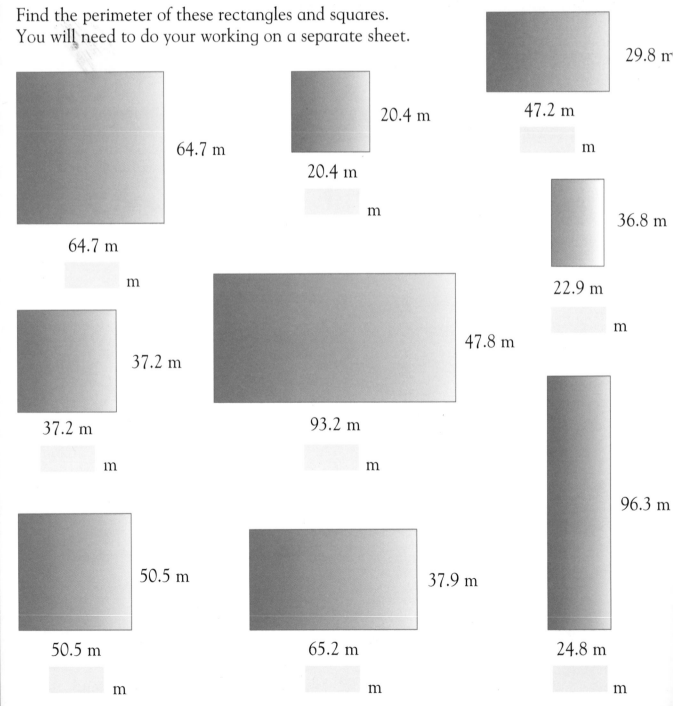

29.8 m

47.2 m

_____ m

64.7 m

64.7 m

_____ m

20.4 m

20.4 m

_____ m

36.8 m

22.9 m

_____ m

37.2 m

37.2 m

_____ m

47.8 m

93.2 m

_____ m

96.3 m

50.5 m

50.5 m

_____ m

37.9 m

65.2 m

_____ m

24.8 m

_____ m

Find the perimeter of these rectangles and squares.
You will need to do your working on a separate sheet.

523.4 cm

311.2 cm

cm

248.9 m

248.9 m

m

462.9 m

110.4 m

m

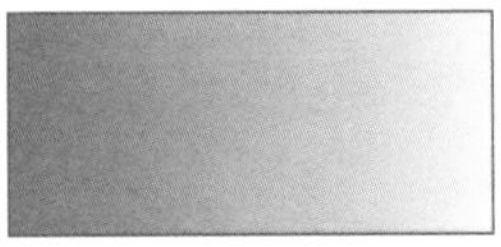

149.2 cm

332.6 cm

cm

514.8 m

326.2 m

m

159.7 cm

159.7 cm

cm

171.5 m

171.5 m

m

138.6 m

99.4 m

m

229.3 m

158.6 m

m

230.3cm

230.3 cm

cm

490.3 cm

337.2 cm

cm

125.2 cm

125.2 cm

cm

Speed problems

How long will it take a cyclist to travel 36 km at a constant speed of 9 kilometres per hour?

4 hours

9 ⟌ 36

Time = Distance ÷ Speed

If a car travelled 150 km at a constant speed in 5 hours, what speed was it travelling at?

30 kph

5 ⟌ 150

Speed = Distance ÷ Time

If a lorry travels for 5 hours at 60 kph, how far does it travel?

5 × 60 = 300 km

Distance = Speed × Time

A car travels along a road at a steady speed of 60 kph. How far will it travel in 6 hours?

A train covers a journey of 960 km in 8 hours. If it travels at a constant speed, how fast is it travelling?

John walks at a steady speed of 6 kph. How long will it take him to travel 24 kilometres?

A car travels at a constant speed of 50 kph. How far will it have travelled in 4 hours?

Melanie completes a cross-country run at a steady speed of 9 kph. If it takes her 3 hours, how far did she run?

Sarah cycles 30 km to her grandmother's house at a steady speed of 10 kph. If she leaves home at 2.00 pm what time will she arrive?

26

Conversion table

This is part of a conversion table that shows how to change pounds to francs when 10 French francs (10fr.) equal £1.

Pounds	Francs
1	10
2	20
3	30

How many francs would you get for £2?   *20fr*

How much is 25fr worth in pounds?   *£2.50*

How many pounds would you get for 40fr?

How many pounds would you get for 85fr?

How much is 1fr worth?

Change £65 into francs.

What is £3.50 in francs?

Change 250fr into pounds.

How many francs could you get for 40p?

Pounds	Francs
1	10
2	20
3	30
4	40
5	50
6	60
7	70
8	80
9	90
10	100

The rate then changes to 8fr to the £1.
The conversion chart now looks like the one shown here.

How many francs are worth £4?

How many pounds can you get for 56fr?

How many francs are worth £9.50?

How many francs can you get for £20?

How many pounds would you get for 120fr?

What is the value of 4fr?

Pounds	Francs
1	8
2	16
3	24
4	32
5	40
6	48
7	56
8	64
9	72
10	80

Interpreting pie charts

32 children voted for their favourite ice-cream flavours.
How many children preferred chocolate?

$\frac{3}{8}$ of 32 is 12

12 children preferred chocolate.

12 children

How many children preferred fudge?

$\frac{1}{8}$ of 32 is 4

4 children preferred fudge.

4 children

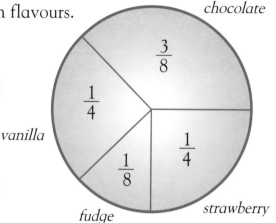

chocolate

$\frac{3}{8}$

$\frac{1}{4}$

vanilla

$\frac{1}{8}$

$\frac{1}{4}$

fudge

strawberry

A class of 30 children voted for their favourite
actor who has played James Bond.

How many preferred Sean Connery?

How many did not like
George Lazenby?

How many more children liked Pierce
Brosnan than liked Roger Moore?

How many children altogether voted
for Sean Connery and Roger Moore?

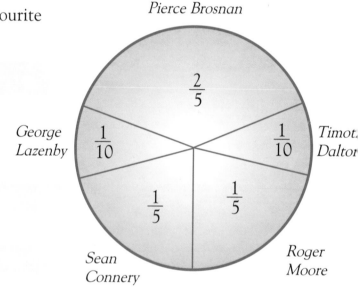

Pierce Brosnan

$\frac{2}{5}$

George
Lazenby $\frac{1}{10}$

$\frac{1}{10}$ Timot.
Daltor

$\frac{1}{5}$

$\frac{1}{5}$

Sean
Connery

Roger
Moore

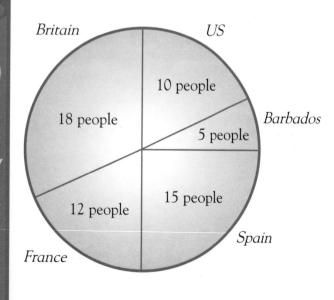

Britain

US

10 people

18 people

Barbados

5 people

12 people

15 people

Spain

France

60 people were asked where they went
on holiday last year. The pie chart shows
the results.

What fraction of people holidayed
in Britain?

What fraction of people holidayed
in the US or Barbados?

What fraction of people did
not go to Spain?

What fraction of people holidayed
in Britain or went to France?

28

Probability scale 0 to 1

Look at this probability line.

Impossible = 0
Poor chance = 0.25
Fair = 0.5
Good chance = 0.75
Certain = 1

Write each letter in the correct place on the probability line.

a. It will be daylight in Southampton at midnight.
b. The sun will come up tomorrow.
c. If I toss a coin it will come down heads.

a			c				b
0	0.25		0.5		0.75		1

0	0.25	0.5	0.75	1

Write each letter in the correct place on the probability line.

a. If I cut a pack of cards I will get a red card.

b. If I cut a pack of cards I will get a diamond.

c. If I cut a pack of cards I will get a diamond, a spade, or a club.

d. If I cut a pack of cards I will get a diamond, a spade, a club, or a heart.

e. If I cut a pack of cards it will be a 15.

0	0.25	0.5	0.75	1

Write each letter in the correct place on the probability line.

a. Next week, Wednesday will be the day after Tuesday.

b. There will be 33 days in February next year.

c. It will snow in London in May.

d. It will snow in London in January.

e. The next person to knock on the door will be a woman.

Likely outcomes

Throw a coin 20 times.

Keep a tally.

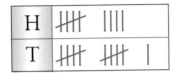

| H | IIII IIII | IIII |
| T | IIII III | IIII IIII I |

What do you notice?

Put your results on a bar chart.

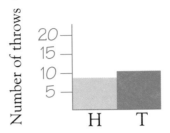

Heads and tails come up roughly the same number of times because there are only two possible outcomes, and they are equally likely.

Predict what you think the outcome would be if you tossed two coins 48 times.

2 heads   times   2 tails   times   1 of each   times

Now throw two coins 48 times yourself and record your results on this tally chart.

2 Heads	
2 Tails	
1 of each	

Draw a bar chart to show your results.

Which result comes up the most often?

Can you explain why some results
are more probable than others?

Naming quadrilaterals

Name this shape.

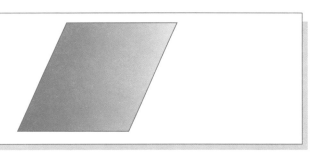

Rhombus

Name these shapes.

Sketch these shapes.

parallelogram   kite

rhombus   trapezium

3D planes of symmetry

If a solid figure is cut into two equal parts, the plane of the cut is called a plane of symmetry.

Draw a plane of symmetry on each of these shapes.

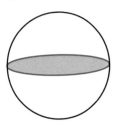

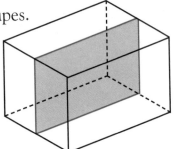

This sphere has been cut into two equal parts by the plane.

This cuboid has been cut into two equal parts by the plane.

Draw a plane of symmetry that is different from the one in the example above on each of these cuboids.

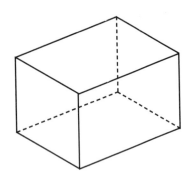

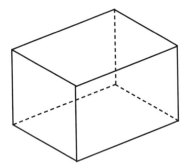

Draw a plane of symmetry on each of these shapes.

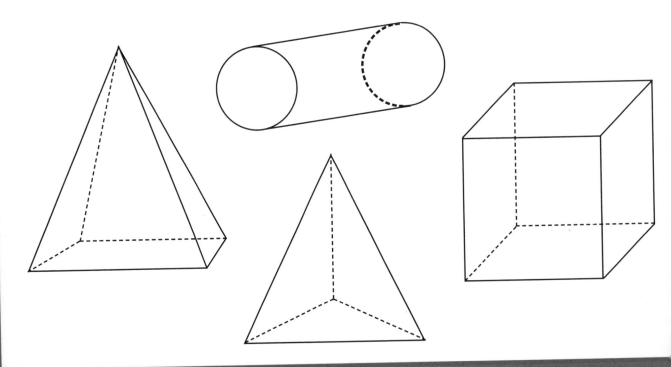

32